THE PAUL DANIELS

Magic annual

JOKER

£2.75

D0411147

CONTENTS

Published in Great Britain by
World International Publishing Limited.
A Pentos Company,
P.O. Box 111, Great Ducie Street, Manchester M60 3BL.
Printed in Italy
SBN 7235 6682 8.

MY WORLD OF MAGIC

There's been plenty of action in my world of magic since I introduced myself to you in last year's annual.

I've appeared at the famous New Tropicana night spot in Las Vegas and entertained an American audience for the first time. After that I went on a three months' tour of the world where I met a lot of magicians and visited many interesting countries.

My month's appearance in Las Vegas, however, really *was* something. I was a bit nervous before I went on but the Americans liked my particular style of humour, especially in one trick where I borrowed a 100 dollar note from a man in the audience.

I then asked a very nice looking girl in the front row to read out the serial number. She did this for me and then sat down.

"Did you hear me say sit down?" I joked. The lady at once leaped to her feet and I was able to get another laugh by saying, "Where I come from women do exactly as they're told."

Just a jest, of course.

I then went ahead, vanished the note and made it appear in a walnut.

I also had a couple of gentlemen up from the audience. One of them, a strapping six footer from Chicago, told me had come to see the show with his parents.

Looking up at him, I was able to get a quick laugh by saying, "Isn't it about time your mum and dad let you out on your own?"

It was the first time an English comedy conjuror of my type had performed in the showbiz capital of the world and they gave me a very warm welcome.

I had a lot of offers to stay there but I wanted to come back to England and the BBC. This is my home and if I did go to America again it would only be for a short visit.

All I really want to do as a performer is to make people happy and be happy myself while I'm doing so. If I can get a few laughs, better still.

Talking of laughs, on page 51 I tell the story of one of the classic feats in magic, Catching the Bullet, and it brings to mind a very funny incident which happened to me a few years ago when I was appearing in Ireland.

A well-known Irish magician sent one of his friends to see me in my dressing room to enquire if I would be kind enough to tell him how to perform this great bullet-catching trick. I was taken aback over this unusual approach and had no idea what to tell my visitor so I decided to play a little joke on him.

Making up the story as I went along, I started off on a long rigmarole as to how he could catch a bullet. I expected him to start laughing after the first few sentences but he took out his pencil and notebook and began writing it all down. My story went like this:

"This is a very dangerous trick. You must begin with pop guns. When your friend finds he can catch the cork from the pop gun he must take a bow and arrow; but he has to use a slack string at first so that the arrow will fly more slowly. Then he can finally tackle a bullet but first remove some of the gunpowder so that it will fly at half speed."

My visitor solemnly wrote down every word, thanked me profusely and left!

I told this story at our Magic Circle Banquet where I was the guest of honour and it got a big laugh.

It may not have occurred to you, but there are only six magical effects in the world and every trick in my magic annual is based on them, apart, of course, from the puzzles and challenges with which to tease your friends.

These six approaches to magic are:

Production of an object.
Vanishing an object.
Transposing two objects.
Levitating an object or a person.
Penetrating one object through another.
Restoration turning something to its original form.

Clever magicians can *produce* cards, thimbles, silks — you name it — out of thin air. They can also *vanish* or *transpose* them. *Levitation* achieves what appears to be the impossible, solid objects or liquids being made to rise mysteriously. They can range from a playing card to a human being. *Penetration* is when a solid object such as a coin passes through a table or someone passes through a solid wall as I did in one of my TV shows. *Restoration* is changing the appearance of an object or person and returning it to its original form.

I hope most of this year's collection of tricks, puzzles and teasers will be new to you and that you'll have fun performing them. But let me stress again that they will all need practice, even the simplest ones. The more you practise the better magician you'll become.

So, welcome to my world of magic and always remember a secret can never remain a secret if you tell it to anyone else.

Let's keep our secrets.

Yours in Magic,

Paul Daniels.

QUICK TRICKS

Here are some quickies for you. They are very easy to perform but effective if presented properly. They're the sort of quick tricks you can perform anywhere. Try them out in your own home before attempting to show them to any of your friends.

The Balanced Egg

This trick really is an old one. Christopher Columbus used to entertain his crew with it on his way to discover America.

The challenge is to balance an egg on its end. To achieve this, do what Christopher Columbus did. Shake the egg hard but carefully so as not to break the shell and this will break up the yolk inside.

The yolk then settles at the bottom of the egg and the extra weight there enables you to balance the egg quite easily.

Get Rich Quick

This is a little mathematical trick that you can work on a friend. Ask him if he'll give you a present of half his profit if you show him how to make an easy £10. Whether he agrees or not, show him the following statement and tell him it's from your bank. Explain, first of all, that you started with a balance of £250.

Withdraw	Balance
£100	£150
75	75
50	25
15	10
10	nil
£250	£260

If your friend adds up your balance after withdrawing the whole £250 he'll have to agree this leaves you with a profit of £10! If he has agreed beforehand to give you half of this, hold out your hand for the fiver he owes you — but don't expect to get it!

The Rice Trick

Here's a little trick that I perform on a video cassette that I've made. It's quite spectacular but no skill is required, it really does work itself.

For a start you need a jar with a narrow neck; the neck must be smaller than the jar itself. Fill the jar with uncooked rice, as much as it will take. Keep packing the rice down so that it's a solid mass.

Thrust a one inch ruler into the centre of the rice. You'll find it won't penetrate very far but if you continue with quick thrusts, withdrawing the ruler each time, then eventually most of it will sink into the rice.

The rice will now have packed itself round the ruler in a solid mass.

Lift the ruler and both rice and jar will rise with it . . . a real aerial suspension (see illustration).

Cube Through The Table

You will have to perform this sitting down. It would make a good trick for a tea party.

Show your friends a lump of sugar wrapped in paper — the sort you find in tea shops and restaurants. Tell them you've discovered that these cubes have some very magical properties: they will pass through solid tables.

Swiftly hit the cube with your clenched fist. It vanishes completely; the wrapper is empty and the cube turns up in your lap. It has gone right through the table!

By this time you'll know enough about magic to realise that nothing of the sort has actually happened even if it looks that way.

Beforehand, you carefully unwrapped the paper cover and took the cube from inside. Then you sealed it up again so that it just *looked* as though it still contained the sugar lump, which was lying on your lap all the time waiting to be discovered.

If you've mastered a little sleight of hand you should be able to let your audience feel a solid cube of sugar inside its wrapper before you start; but you'll have to be clever enough to switch the genuine wrapped piece for the empty fake wrapper. It can be done but it takes practice.

The Balancing Coins

Put a couple of thick rimmed tumblers on the table with a strip of stiff paper between them as shown in the drawing.

Balance a couple of 10p pieces on top of each glass.

Challenge your friends to remove the paper without touching the coins or changing their position on the edge of the glasses.

To make this happen, strike the centre of the paper with your right forefinger. Bring it down sharply and the paper will fly away leaving the coins still in position. You may need to moisten the underside of your finger just before you hit the centre of the paper.

Reds and Blacks

Write on a piece of paper "The heap of red cards will have the same number of cards as the heap of black". Have someone hold your prediction, sealed in an envelope.

Using 50 cards, 25 red and 25 black, have them mixed thoroughly. Invite someone to remove two cards at a time and if both are black put them in one heap; if both are red put them in another pile. Two cards of different colours go in a separate, third heap.

When all 50 cards have been sorted in this way you'll find both heaps containing cards of the same colour will *always have the same number of cards in them.*

To repeat, secretly steal a few cards of the same colour, say, black. This time predict "The black heap will have four fewer cards than the red".

Knifed

Have one of your audience choose a card and lay it aside. They should be holding the pack when they make their choice. Next, they cut the pack in two sections; both sections remain face down on the table. You then ask, "Which pile do you want?" When they have made their choice you point to the pile and ask, "You mean this pile?" When they answer, "Yes," get them to put their chosen card face downwards on the pack of their choice.

You place the other half on top of the chosen pile. Thus, the chosen card is hidden in the centre of the pack.

Then announce "I will tap the pack with my magic wand and the pack will divide at your card."

Give the pack a tap and, sure enough, it will split at the chosen card.

The secret: a few grains of salt in your pocket. Pick them up between your thumb and second finger to enable you secretly to drop the salt on the top of the pile of cards your friend selects as you point to it with your forefinger.

A tap on the whole pack will cause it to swing into two sections and then the chosen card will be at the bottom of the top pack.

11

The Balanced Top

Challenge your friends to balance a 10p piece on the edge of a £1 note. Unless they know the secret they will be unable to do so.

This is how it's done: fold the note lengthways down the middle and place it on the table. Make a good crease in the fold and then fold it again so that it makes the letter V. Have the two sides of the note on the table with the edge uppermost.

Place the coin on the top edge and then slowly ease the two ends of the note so that it stretches into one straight line.

Your coin, if you are careful, will remain balanced in the centre of the folded note.

Hoop and Bottle Trick

Make a hoop of stiff paper and stand it on the mouth of a wine bottle. Place a small coin on top of the hoop just above the neck of the bottle and challenge someone to get the coin inside the bottle.

All you need do is to take your wand and hit the inside of the hoop with a quick sideways blow. The hoop will spin away and the coin will fall into the bottle.

The Spinning Egg

Challenge someone to spin an egg. They wi fail. But when you pick up an egg they'll b astonished to find that you can spin it with ease.

This is because, unknown to your friend, yo are using a hard boiled egg. Try it and see hou well it spins.

The Egg In The Bottle Mystery

Show your friends a clear, glass wine bottle. Inside there is an egg, much wider than the neck of the bottle. How did it get there?

To achieve this, soak a hard-boiled egg in vinegar until the shell softens and the egg becomes pliable. Be patient — it may take a week! Then pull the egg into a sausage shape and push it into the bottle previously filled with water. Pour off the water.

The egg will resume its normal appearance.

The Hot Coin

Show your audience some coins in a dish and have one of them select a coin and hold it in the hand while you either turn your back or you are blindfolded.

Have your assistant hold the coin tightly in his hand while he concentrates on the date on the coin. Suggest he repeats this date to himself a few times.

When he has done this he puts the coin back in the dish with the others. On turning round, you at once select the chosen coin.

Explanation: you have so arranged things that your friend holds the coin tightly for quite a while. When you pick up the coins one by one you can easily tell which coin had been selected — it will be the warmest one.

The Penetrating Thimble

Show your audience a thimble on the forefinger of your left hand. Place a handkerchief over the thimble, reach underneath and take the thimble from the hidden left forefinger, replacing it on the finger again on the other side of the handkerchief.

Your audience now see the thimble on top of your forefinger but separated by the handkerchief.

Whisk the handkerchief upwards by the four corners with the right hand and, believe it or not, the thimble is back on your left forefinger.

Two thimbles are used, one smaller than the other. When you start you have both thimbles on your left finger, one inside the other. It's the larger one that you remove and place over the handkerchief, leaving the smaller one to be discovered later.

Cut and Restored String

Secretly cut a small slit in one side of a drinking straw. Show your audience a piece of string just longer than the straw and thread it through the straw. Fold the straw in half with the slit downwards.

While doing this, pull the string slightly downwards through the slit so that it is, in fact, separate.

Now, using scissors, put the point of the bottom blade above the string and cut through the straw. To your audience it will appear as though you are also cutting the string.

Pull the straw from both ends and show that although the straw has been cut in two, the string remains in one piece.

STRING

The Water in Glass Trick

Fill a glass tumbler with water — right to the brim. Ask your friend what he thinks will happen if you turn the glass upside down. He's bound to say, "The water will run out."

But if you place a piece of cardboard over the top of the glass and then turn it upside down the water stays in the glass and not a drop is spilt.

The Endless Cotton

Put a cotton reel of thread in your outside pocket. Using a needle, run the thread through the pocket and up inside your coat. Now push it through so that the thread can be seen hanging down from outside your coat.

This looks like a loose thread. Someone is bound to try and pick it off. Imagine their surprise when the thread continues to unravel and will continue until the cotton reel is exhausted.

15

The Rising Water Trick

Half fill a saucer with water. Place a coin in the water. The challenge: remove the coin without wetting the fingers.

When everyone fails, take a small piece of paper and screw it into a ball. Light the paper and while it is still burning place a glass tumbler over it, leaving the coin outside.

The tiny fire is extinguished; the water rises inside the glass and the coin is removed.

Please do not attempt this trick without help from an adult because of the fire element.

The Spinning Ball

You can spin a ball around an opened umbrella if you previously have the ball on a thread which is attached to the tip of the umbrella.

Practise throwing the ball on top of the umbrella as you open it.

Balancing a Handkerchief

The performer borrows a handkerchief; twists it into a rope; balances it on his finger.

To make this possible, first try to balance the 'kerchief — and fail. It falls on your table. Here you have a small length of wire. Pick up the handkerchief, also pick up the wire.

Twine the cloth around the wire and it will balance quite easily. To avoid detection, paint the wire white.

The Bouncing Handkerchief

You should get a laugh with this one.

Sew a rubber ball into the middle of your handkerchief. Then, after a couple of tricks, take the hankie out of your pocket and throw it on the ground.

It will immediately bounce back into your hand.

17

The Coathanger Trick

Take a wooden coathanger with a crossbar and hold it hooked round your right forefinger. Balance a 10p piece on the crossbar. Swing the hanger backwards and forwards and increase the speed until you have the hanger spinning in complete circles.

The coin stays in position because of the centrifugal force.

This trick can also be done with a wire coat-hanger but you'll need more practice.

The Spinning Hankie

To throw a handkerchief in the air, catch it on the end of your wand and twirl it around, simply have a needle point embedded in the end of the wand.

This will catch the cloth and act as a pivot as you whirl the handkerchief.

To Tear a Telephone Directory in Two

It's not as hard as you think and you don't have to be a strong person to achieve this.

Any soft-backed directory can be torn in half if you first bake it in the oven so that all the moisture is extracted.

You can do the same with a pack of cards. But don't do this on your own. You must get an adult's help because of the fire risk.

The Drink Trick

Have a glass of water covered with an inverted glass so that they look like a glass cocktail shaker. Have the bottom glass about three quarters full. Challenge a friend to drink the water without using his hands to touch either the top glass or the one underneath.

The secret: lean forward and grip the top glass between your chin and your chest. Lift this glass carefully and place it on the table. Now pick up the bottom glass using your teeth to grip the rim. You'll find if you tilt your head backwards you can easily drink the water. Have both glasses near the end of the table for you'll need to sit down to achieve this "Look—No Hands" trick.

The Prince Charles Note

This is something you will probably have to work out with a grown-up. For a start, you'll need two five pound notes.

Take the first note and fold it as shown in my illustration, i.e. with the Duke of Wellington's nose and eyes showing.

Fold the second note as shown, i.e. with only the bottom half of the Queen's face to be seen.

Place the top half of the Duke's head to meet the bottom half of the Queen's face and put your thumb as in the drawing.

Ask someone who this reminds them of and nine out of ten will tell you 'Prince Charles'.

Uncanny, isn't it?

The Spinning 10p

Put a playing card on the forefinger of your friend's left hand, then balance a 10p coin on top of that. Invite your friend to remove the card without moving the coin.

To make this happen, just strike the edge of the card with a quick flick of the second finger of your right hand, drawing this finger back with your thumb on the nail to give it extra power. Release your finger so that it hits the edge of the card and this will send it spinning with the coin left steadily balanced on the forefinger.

Numbers Up

If you have a pocket calculator you might like to try out this little trick on your friends.

First mark up the numbers 1-2-3-4-5-6-7-9 on the display panel. Note the number 8 is *not* used.

Then ask a friend to give you any number between 1 and 9.

Tell him you are now going to show him something very remarkable. Give him the calculator and get him to multiply the numbers shown by 0.9.

Then get him to multiply this second number by the number he had originally chosen. The result: every digit will be this original number. For example, if your friend's number is 8, he will finish up with this: 1-2-3-4-5-6-7-9 multiplied by 0.9 multiplied by 8 equals 88888888.

If your calculator doesn't have a floating decimal point then enter 1-2-3-4-5-6-7-9 at the start.

The Vanishing Stamp

Here's how to make a postage stamp vanish — or appear to.

Fill a glass tumbler with water, about two thirds is enough. Place it over a stamp lying face upwards on the table. Make sure the stamp is in the centre of the glass of water and if you now place a saucer on top of the glass you'll find the stamp has completely vanished!

To bring it back just lift the tumbler.

The Mystic Sum

Write down these figures or get a typist friend to copy them for you. Have them on a small card in your pocket.

```
1000
  20
  30
1000
1030
1000
  20
————
4100
```

Show the card to a friend, covering all the numbers except the top line. Ask him to tell you what the number is. Now show the next line and get him to add the two lines together and remember the total. Then he must do the same with the next line until he finally has to add 20 to his total.

Keep your finger on the total throughout and when you ask him to give you his total most people will give you 5000 as the correct answer.

Show them the total on the card— and prove them wrong. But they must do the addition in their head and not use a calculator.

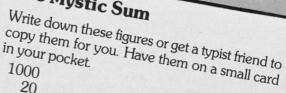

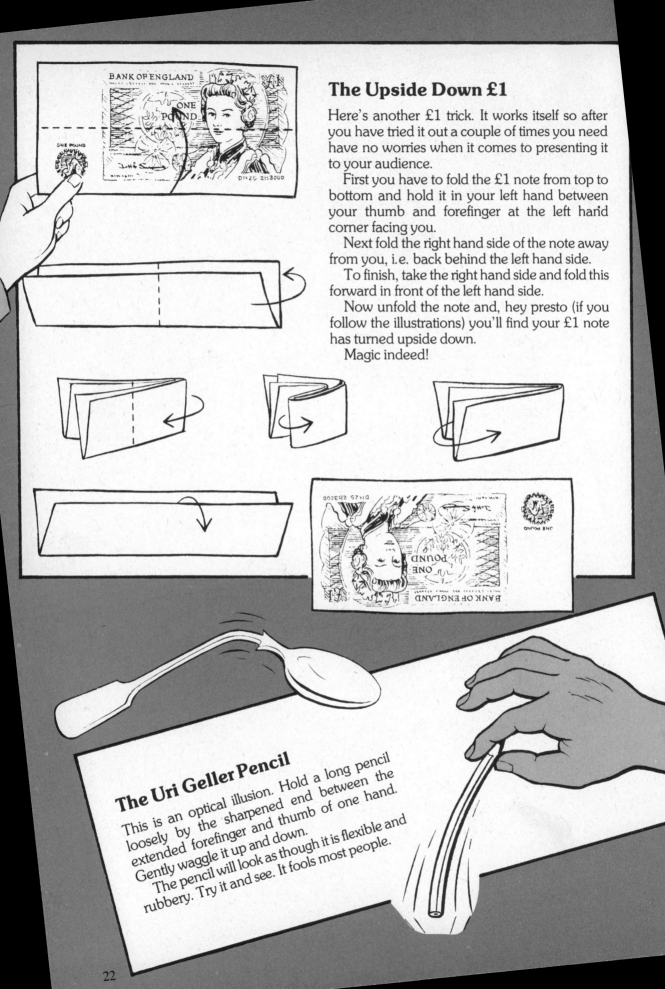

The Upside Down £1

Here's another £1 trick. It works itself so after you have tried it out a couple of times you need have no worries when it comes to presenting it to your audience.

First you have to fold the £1 note from top to bottom and hold it in your left hand between your thumb and forefinger at the left hand corner facing you.

Next fold the right hand side of the note away from you, i.e. back behind the left hand side.

To finish, take the right hand side and fold this forward in front of the left hand side.

Now unfold the note and, hey presto (if you follow the illustrations) you'll find your £1 note has turned upside down.

Magic indeed!

The Uri Geller Pencil

This is an optical illusion. Hold a long pencil loosely by the sharpened end between the extended forefinger and thumb of one hand. Gently waggle it up and down.

The pencil will look as though it is flexible and rubbery. Try it and see. It fools most people.

22

Oranges and Glasses

Use four wine glasses, four corks and four small oranges. Place a piece of cardboard over the glasses, a cork over each glass and an orange on top. Give the board a swift, sharp blow and it will fly away leaving the oranges to fall into the glasses.

The Jumping Band

Show your audience that you have a rubber band around your first two fingers. Close your hand to make a fist and the band is still seen to be in its original position.

Open your hand and your audience will see the band has jumped over to the last two fingers. This little pocket puzzler can be easily performed if you follow my simple instructions.

First place the rubber band below the knuckles over your first two fingers, then stretch the band forwards with the other hand. Next, bend your fingers so that they slip inside the loop. Finally, open your hand and the rubber band will leave your first two fingers and, instead, cover the last two.

Practise this until you can do it in one uninterrupted move. It'll fool most of your friends.

The Floating Sugar Cube

To prepare this, wet the sides of half-a-dozen sugar lumps and put them in a pile so that they all stick together.

Next time you have a cup of tea put this pile secretly into the cup. It will at once appear as though the top lump is floating on the surface.

Say some magic words. Gradually the top lump will sink below the surface as the lumps beneath melt.

But, unless you have a very sweet tooth, don't drink the tea.

The Wallpaper Trick

You can play this trick on someone either in your own home or when you're visiting friends. But make sure they have a sense of humour.

Take a large piece of white paper, fold it in half, tear round the edges to give a ragged appearance (illustration A).

Slightly dampen the bottom half of the paper so that it sticks to the wallpaper in your room. Allow the top half to drop down as in illustration B.

Anyone entering the room will think you've torn the wallpaper.

THE INDIAN ROPE TRICK

The Indian Rope Trick is the most famous trick in the world but has it ever been performed in the way it has been described? I doubt it.

Various versions have been talked about for years, in fact the original account goes back to 1355. It was written by Mohmed and included in his book *Travels in Asia and Africa*.

Mohmed described how a Chinese magician entertained guests at a special celebration by throwing a wooden ball into the sky. A rope, made of strips of leather, was attached to the ball which eventually disappeared into the clouds.

The magician then introduced his assistant, a small boy, who climbed the leather rope until he too disappeared into the clouds.

The magician called on him to return and when he failed to do so he too climbed sky-wards. Then followed the gruesome sight of the boy's limbs being thrown to the ground.

These were followed by the magician himself reappearing by sliding down the upright leather strips. He picked up the boy's limbs, fitted them together and when they were all assembled the boy got to his feet . . . unharmed.

Mohmed himself related how such a spectacle gave him a mild heart attack. He had to be given a stiff drink to restore him to normality. Looking round, he saw that the rest of the company were quite unmoved by such a startling performance.

"It's a trick, my friend," his companion told him. "Nothing else."

Mohmed's account is the first by anyone claiming to have actually *seen* the Indian Rope Trick. In 1556, two hundred years later, a book written by Johann Weir gave an account of a similar happening.

According to Weir, a German magician was so disgusted by the public's contributions towards his expenses for his street performance that he told them he was off to seek his reward in heaven.

The man then threw a length of rope in the air. It remained rigid and the magician led his small horse to the rope whereupon it ran straight up it towards the sky. The magician followed, then the magician's wife and her maid . . . all three hand in hand.

This was all too much for the assembled on-lookers who stood there looking skywards. A man passing by enquired what had happened and when the crowd told him he burst out laughing.

"You've been tricked, my friends," he told them. "I've just seen the wizard enter a tavern just down the road."

Janangir, the Emperor of Hindustani from 1605 to 1627, tells of a similar happening in his memoirs. It took place in the courtyard of his palace in Delhi. On this occasion seven magicians from Bengal went one better by throwing a metal chain straight upwards and vanishing a number of animals, including a lion and a tiger, into space. The creatures just ran up the chain and disappeared!

Pu Sing Ling, a famous Chinese historian, records in 1650 that he had seen a version of the Indian Rope Trick twenty years previously when he was a child. Pu said he'd seen a Chinese conjuror order his boy assistant to climb a suspended rope to fetch fruit from heaven. The assistant climbed the rope and a large peach fell to the ground. This was followed by various limbs from the boy's body. The wizard gathered them up, placed them in a box and after saying a magic spell the young assistant stepped from the box with all his limbs intact.

There have been similar stories of the Indian Rope Trick ever since, but no one can be found who has actually witnessed such a miracle.

Every foreign magician who has visited India has sought in vain to find an Indian colleague who could perform this mystery. Many of them have been able to reproduce it on the stage but that's something quite different. The essential appeal of the Indian Rope Trick as it has been described through the ages is that it has always been performed in the open, well apart from trees or buildings.

The Magic Circle offered £1,000 back in the thirties to any Indian magician who would come to London and perform the trick in Lords cricket ground.

The late Bertram Mills, famed circus pro-prietor, made it £10,000.

But the challenge has never been taken up. The Indian Rope Trick has remained unseen . . . by anyone.

It's a myth, something that never happened.

The earliest known account of a magical performance is contained in a very ancient document in the State Museum of East Berlin. The document itself is dated 1700BC although the incident it describes took place five thousand years ago, so the document must be a copy of the original account.

The ancient scroll tells how Cheops, who built the Great Pyramid, was told by one of his sons that a great magician called Dedi lived further down the Nile. He was supposed to be

110 years old and every day he was alleged to eat a whole shoulder of beef, five hundred loaves, washed down by a hundred jugs of beer!

The Egyptian king was determined that Dedi should give a Royal Command Performance before him, so he sent his son to invite Dedi to come to the palace at Memphis. Two royal barges were sent and the young prince explained to the magician that his father would like Dedi to return with him. He would become an honoured member of the royal household and receive a royal funeral at the end of his days.

Dedi agreed to the proposal and on his arrival at the palace he at once arranged to give a magical performance for his host.

He performed some incredible tricks with a goose, a pelican and an ox, vanishing them and making them appear at will. He also did the same with a lion.

Dedi is certainly the first entertainer in the history of magic to achieve a write-up of his act, and he gave his show 5,000 years ago!

Many other magicians have followed in his footsteps over the centuries. In 200AD, Alciphon, who lived in Athens, recorded his astonishment when he saw a conjuror do a trick with three bowls and some white pebbles. Here's his description:

"He placed the pebbles one by one under the dishes. Then, I do not know how, he made them appear all together under one.

"At one time he made them disappear from beneath the dishes and showed them in his mouth. Next, when he swallowed them, he brought those who stood nearest him into the middle and then pulled one stone from the nose, another from the ear and another from the head of the man standing near him.

"Finally, he caused the stones to vanish from the sight of everyone."

Any magician would recognise this sleight of hand routine as an early version of the classic Cups and Balls effect, as popular today, and just as mystifying in the hands of a competent performer as it was all those years ago.

WORLD TOUR

On my three month world tour I visited lots of exciting places — Calcutta, Bombay, Hong Kong, Japan, Singapore, Bahrain, Cairo and then back to London.

I took more than 2,000 colour photographs of my adventures in the East and some of them are here in this book.

One of the funniest moments was aboard a pleasure steamer going up the Nile. They had a talent contest aboard so I decided to enter.

No one knew who I was so I just did a few tricks with whatever objects were lying around . . . a pack of cards, paper serviettes and similar articles.

At the end the captain told me, "I think you should have all the prizes."

Then I told him I was a magician and I hadn't really entered the contest to win a prize — just to entertain my fellow passengers.

In Singapore I did a show in the home of a British Airways executive and included the famous Cups and Balls routine, the world's oldest known trick.

It went down well, too.

In Tokyo, although I didn't have any props, I agreed to appear on television. The trouble was, however, that those Japanese TV chaps couldn't make up their minds what they wanted

me to do. To get them to decide what trick they wanted performed in front of the cameras was really impossible — a trick in itself.

Nothing is ever decided on the spot, everything has to wait till tomorrow.

Whatever we discussed had to be referred to some big boss somewhere, whom I never met. This seems to be the Japanese way of life and they even have a joke about it that only three people in the whole of Japan ever make decisions — everything is sent on to them to handle and make the final decision.

The TV producer they gave me wasn't very helpful either. He wanted me to perform a few tricks and then show everyone how they were done!

He thought it would be a loss of face on his part if he didn't do this. He didn't want to be mystified and he didn't want the viewers mystified either!

Nothing like this had ever happened to me on my shows in England, or anywhere else for that matter. I found this attitude quite extraordinary.

But then the whole way of life in Japan is very different to ours. I spent two weeks there and wish it could have been longer.

So why not join me on a colourful day trip to visit some of the places of interest?

This is Kyoko, who is going to be your guide. She's carrying a flag so that you'll be able to find her easily and won't get lost.

First, we're going to look at some Japanese gardens. The Japanese are famous for their skill in planning these. Every leaf is cultivated to achieve the effect they want. Nothing is allowed to grow naturally. Notice the way the trees have been placed to provide a background of peace and serenity to the still waters of the lake.

This three-tiered palace has been built by a wealthy Japanese as his retirement home. With such beauty awaiting him I can well imagine that he'll be taking early retirement.

Let's pause for a moment to appreciate the clever way these bamboo trees have been positioned above this tiled roof. They make a wonderful background. The growth of each tree has been controlled to the exact shape and size to achieve this effect.

This is my encounter with a deer. They are very friendly creatures and have been trained to incline their heads in a traditional Japanese bow when receiving a gift of food.

Buddhism has been Japan's main religion since the 6th century and there are many beautiful Buddhist temples and shrines to be seen. This golden Buddha is a fine example.

Like everywhere else, weddings are big events in Japan. There's a wedding reception at our hotel when we return and these three guests are delighted we should want to take their picture.

A Japanese rock group? Not really, just the musicians who are to entertain us at the concert for which we have tickets for the evening performance.

The star of the show — a traditional, masked dancer performing a centuries old routine . . . a fitting climax for our one day tour of Tokyo.

P.S. I took the pictures. A deer friend took the one of me!!

CARD TRICKS

Playing cards have always been a favourite with magicians. More tricks are done with cards than anything else. Every house has a pack of cards somewhere and it's always more fun to use other people's cards than your own, just to show that a genuine and not a trick pack has been used.

In this section I'm going to show you how to do a number of card tricks. None of them use sleight of hand and I don't pretend they are by any means new or my own invention. But I do know that if they are presented properly they will baffle most people, unless they know the secret.

TO DISCOVER A CHOSEN CARD

Deal the cards in three piles, face upwards, and have one of your audience select a card. Ask him to remember in which heap it is but not to tell you.

After dealing 21 cards, discard the others in the pack as they won't be required. Ask your friend to tell you which heap contains the chosen card. Place this heap between the other two and then deal out the cards in three piles as before.

Now enquire again which pack has the chosen card, place the pack in the middle and deal again for the third time. You are still dealing the cards face upwards, so just note the middle or fourth card of each pile. One of these three cards will be the one your friend has selected. Ask your friend where his card is positioned. Once he has told you the pile, you know at once that it is the middle card of that heap.

MIDDLE CARD

TO VANISH A CARD AND PRODUCE IT SOMEWHERE ELSE

This needs to be performed with a pack of small-sized cards, the kind used for bridge. At the start, when no one is looking, moisten the back of your left hand with your tongue. Make sure your hand is clean first!

Then get someone in your audience to shuffle the cards. Place the pack face downwards on the table and ask a spectator to look at the top card. Have him place the back of his left hand on the pack and then put the palm of his right hand on top to put extra pressure on the pack.

Show him just what to do yourself before he does this. Now, since you have secretly moistened the back of your left hand, the card will stick to your hand when you have finished

this demonstration.

Everyone will be crowding round to watch the cards on the table so take your time over this and casually put your hands behind your back. This will enable you to take the card from the back of your left hand with your right and place it in your pocket. If you're clever enough you might get a chance to put it under a cushion or some other hiding place.

When your friend has carried out your instructions, let him stay with his hands pressing the pack for a moment or two as you explain that you will now make his selected card fly away from the pack and appear elsewhere. At your command, your companion lifts his hands, turns over the top card and finds that his chosen card has indeed vanished! All you have to do to impress your audience is to produce it from wherever you have hidden it.

DO AS I DO

This is something very different in card tricks and caused tremendous interest when it was first performed some years ago. You use two packs of cards and you face your assistant across a table, each with a pack lying face downwards in front of you.

Every move that you make your assistant has to repeat. Here's what you do:-

Shuffle the pack.

Exchange the packs.

Shuffle again.

Exchange again.

Take any card from your pack, look at it and replace it on top of the pack. Cut the cards.

Exchange the packs.

Look through the cards. Take out the one just chosen from the other pack and place it face down on the table.

Since your assistant has been duplicating your movements throughout, you now have two cards on the table — yours and his, face downwards.

Turn up your card. He turns up his. They are identical.

To achieve this miracle just remember the bottom card in the pack when you first shuffle the spectator's pack. As you hand it back to him for him to choose his card you know that, on cutting the cards, his card will be immediately below the card you spotted.

When you next exchange packs you just look through his pack and pick out the card below the indicator card. That's the one you put face down and that will be the same one that your assistant will select from his pack.

You can forget about the card you yourself chose originally. That's what we magicians call misdirection.

THE ROYAL GATHERING

For this effect take the court cards of the pack (the kings, queens and knaves) and lay them face upwards in three rows of four each. Don't draw attention to the fact that you are placing them in a special order, though in fact you are.

Remember that in the first row you mustn't have two of the same suit. Start the second row with a card of the same suit with which you ended the first. Let the second card in this row be of the same suit as the first of the first row and so on.

The third row starts with the same suit which ended the second row, the second card will be the same suit as the first of the second row and so on.

Now pick up the cards in vertical rows, starting with the last card of the bottom row: left to right. You can cut the cards as many times as you like, but not shuffle them.

Finally, deal them in four heaps and you'll find the king, queen and knave of each suit will all be together.

Try this with the cards in your hand while reading these instructions. It's a trick that works itself and can be very puzzling to others.

THE JUMPING QUEENS

Place the queen of hearts in a hat. Call this hat no.1. Now place the queen of spades in another hat — hat no.2. Say your favourite magic words and produce the queen of spades from hat no.1 and the queen of hearts from hat no.2.

To accomplish this just paste a duplicate of each card on the back of the other. Turn them round, *inside* each hat, before you bring them out.

PASTE BACKS TOGETHER

HALF AND HALF

Your pack of cards is divided in half by one of your audience. Each half is then shuffled. A card is taken from one section and shuffled into the other. You look through this half of the pack and at once produce the selected card.

How is it done? Well, divide the pack beforehand: reds in one section, blacks in the other. Use the joker to separate them. Discard this card at the start, saying that you won't need the joker and the pack is then all set up and separated as required.

THE FRIENDLY KINGS

One king is placed on top of the pack. You place another on the bottom and the third in the centre — all face downwards.

Cut the cards, then spread them out face upwards. The three kings are together in the centre of the pack.

Explanation: the fourth king is already on top of the pack. This is your secret. Just show the other three kings quickly when you start the trick. No one will spot your deceit.

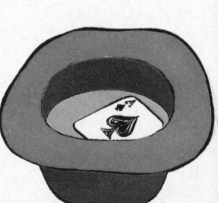

HATS AND CARDS TRICK

Place a hat on the floor. Challenge your friend to stand over the hat and drop as many cards as possible inside. They must be dropped singly, one at a time.

Most people will drop the cards by holding one end and letting them fall lengthwise. The performer, however, can drop his cards into the hat every time simply by holding each card flat between thumb and fingers and letting it fall directly into the hat.

THE THREE CARD TRICK

Three cards, memorised by the audience, are turned face downwards. Each is turned face upwards when the audience see that two are as before but the third has changed suit.

Explanation: the centre card must always be the ace of hearts. Hold the three cards as shown in the illustration and it will *appear* to be the ace of diamonds. From then onwards the trick works itself.

PREDICTION CARD

Have someone in your audience name any card. In this case let's suppose they've chosen the six of clubs.

You then reach in your pocket and produce cards that exactly add up to the value of the card chosen and also indicate its suit.

To achieve this impressive effect all you have to do is to have in your pocket four cards: the 8 of spades; 4 of hearts; 2 of clubs and ace of diamonds. You'll note that each card represents a different suit and the value of each card can be used to equal the value of any card chosen. You would count jack as eleven; queen as twelve and king as thirteen.

Here are two examples: For the six of clubs you would bring out the two of clubs to give you the suit and the value of two. Next, bring out the four of hearts and you have increased the total value of the two cards to six, which was the value of the chosen card.

Let's say the card chosen is the jack of spades. Here you would bring out the eight of spades, then the two of clubs and then the ace of diamonds. The first card would give the suit and the value of eight. The next two cards would increase the number from eight to eleven, thus giving the total required for the jack of spades.

I suggest you have all four cards on top of the pack at the start, then place them in your pocket before inviting your friend to think of a card.

When he has done so, tell him that the cards you have placed in your pocket will add up to the very card he has selected. Not only that, they'll tell the suit as well.

Don't make it too obvious how many cards you have placed in your pocket. Thus, if the chosen card happens to be the eight of clubs you need only bring out two cards: the two of clubs for the suit and the eight of spades for the value.

If anyone selects a court card, explain what their values are: eleven for a jack; twelve for a queen and thirteen for a king.

When, by some good fortune, someone picks the actual card you have in your pocket, produce it with a flourish and enjoy a standing ovation.

THE THREE IN ONE DIVINATION

This is a very impressive trick based on a very old idea. The performer begins by dealing a few cards in three separate piles. The cards lie face downwards and he then takes from his pocket one small folded slip of paper. This slip is placed beside one of the small heaps.

Explain that each heap is different: two of them contain an odd number of cards, the other has an even number. No two are exactly alike. Finally, tell your friends: "As a magician I can tell in advance just what heap you are going to select and I have written my prediction on this piece of folded paper."

One of your onlookers then selects any pile. You open the folded piece of paper and show that you have correctly predicted which heap they would select.

Now for the subtle explanation: the first heap has seven cards; the middle has four and the last has three sevens (say the seven of diamonds, seven of hearts, seven of clubs).

On your prediction you have written "You will select the seven heap".

Thus, if your friend chooses the first heap of seven cards, just pick up the prediction and you'll be right.

If he chooses the heap with the three sevens you'll also be right.

What happens if he picks the middle heap with the four cards? This is easily solved: just pick up the prediction and keep your thumb over the letter "S". It will then read "You will select the even heap". (see illustration).

Clever stuff, eh?

MENTAL WIZARDRY

Put the following cards in a row: the king of spades; seven of clubs; ace of diamonds; four of hearts and nine of diamonds.

Tell your friend to concentrate on one card. He can change his mind if he chooses but he must finally select one of the five cards and think of just that one.

Then pick up the cards, lay the four of hearts face downwards on the table and ask him to name his card.

The odds are in your favour that he will name the four of hearts, the exact card you have placed before him!

I'm not going to promise you it will always work. If it doesn't don't pause when he names his card and it's not the four of hearts, immediately say "correct" and pick it up without showing it, put it back in the pack and shuffle it. You'll get a laugh anyway.

43

THE HORSE THIEVES

This trick has a little story running through it. You'll find it fun to tell it to your friends and as the trick practically works itself you shouldn't find it hard to perform.

First show your audience a couple of empty hats and explain that these hats represent stables. Put a jack into each hat and explain that the two cards represent a couple of cattle rustlers who are hiding in the stables with the intention of stealing some horses.

The horses are represented by five more cards (don't use court cards). Show them to your audience and place them face down.

"The cattle rustlers steal them in turn," you explain.

And you take the five cards and place them, backs to the audience, in the two hats separately; one goes in the left hat, another in the right, the third in the left, the next in the right until you finish with the final fifth card in the left hat.

The story continues: "Everything is fine until the cattle thieves think they hear the sheriff and his posse galloping up to the ranch. The thieves quickly return the horses."

Now you bring out the cards (face down again) from the hats in this order: right, left, right, left, right.

"But it turns out to be a false alarm and when the rustlers find there is no sheriff around they once more steal the horses."

Here, you again put the cards in the hats in this order: left, right, left, right, left.

"But at this point, hearing a noise, the rancher himself turns up to see what's happening. But those cattle rustlers were too clever for him. For in one

stable there were all the horses and in the other, all he found was a couple of cowboys having a sleep."

While saying this you pick out five cards from the hat on the left and the two jacks from the hat on the right.

Work this out with some cards and you'll see just how easy it is to achieve this switch around.

All you have to do is to take the jack from the hat on the right and lay if face down as the first card when you are replacing the horses in their stables. Then take a card from the left, another from the right, the other jack from the left and

the final card from the right.

Remember you are only showing the backs of the cards throughout. Keep the faces towards *you* — not the audience.

When the horses are stolen from the stable for the last time, put the top card in the hat on your left; the next card, a jack, in the hat on your right; the third card in the left, followed by the jack in the right and the last card in the left.

It may take you a little time to get the hang of all this. But, believe me, it's well worth the effort. The more you practise the moves while talking, the more proficient you'll become.

CHUNG LING SOO

One of the most colourful magicians of his day was an American performer whose real name was Billy Robinson. He toured the world with his magic show and there isn't a magician in the world who hasn't heard of him. Yet very few know his name. In the world of magic he remains . . . Chung Ling Soo.

One of Soo's most famous posters.

Chung Ling Soo — in reality Billy Robinson, an American magician — always wore a bald wig for his stage appearances.

This great performer always appeared before his audiences dressed as a Chinese mandarin. Outside the theatre he maintained his Chinese pose and whenever he was interviewed by the Press he spoke in pidgin English. Sometimes he strung together a lot of meaningless words pretending he was Chinese. He even had his manager pretend to translate them for him.

He lived in Lonsdale Road, Barnes, Middlesex, and one of the rooms was fitted out in Chinese style with carved Chinese cabinets, silk pictures on the walls and a large throne-like chair where Soo used to place himself before receiving visitors.

At the end of a large garden there was a three-storey building where Soo organised the building of his stage illusions. He also had a small menagerie in the grounds for his rabbits, doves and other livestock that he used in his stage act.

This was in the heyday of British music hall and Soo could earn as much as £600 a week; a lot of money in those days.

He hadn't always been so affluent. Back in the '80s he began his working life as a metal worker in New York. Then, as a teenager, he became interested in magic and called himself "Robinson, the Man of Mystery". He worked in vaudeville for some years and then married a young dancer and singer, Olive Path, nicknamed Dot.

The two of them put together a new style act using what is known as the Black Art principle, a technique which is still in use today. It was Robinson who was first to perform it in the USA.

The performers, dressed in black, work against a black background with lights facing the audience. This prevents the audience seeing what is actually happening on the stage as the performers move chairs, float tables, disappear bodies and achieve many other mysterious happenings. The performers, because of their clothes and background, remain invisible . . . only the articles they move around are seen.

Billy Robinson now called himself Achmed Ben Ali. He was such a hit that Harry Kellar, a top line illusionist, signed him up to join his own stage show. Billy Robinson changed his name again — to Nana Sahib.

Later he joined Kellar's great rival, Alexander Herrmann. Again he changed his name. Again he picked an oriental role. Nana Sahib was now known as Abdul Khan.

Herrmann the Great, as he was called, taught Billy a great deal, and Billy became one of his most valuable stage assistants. He also taught Billy to impersonate him; if Herrmann was absent from a show at any time, Billy would take over and no one would be any the wiser.

After Herrmann's death, the Robinsons stayed with his widow and then, after the show had been taken over by a nephew, they left to work on their own.

It was during this period that something very novel happened in the world of performing magicians. A Chinese magician was booked into a New York vaudeville theatre and for the first time American audiences saw a complete eastern magical presentation.

The magician called himself Ching Ling Foo and had a whole troupe of Chinese assistants including his own wife and daughter.

His most startling trick was to produce a huge bowl of water from nowhere and he challenged anyone to duplicate the trick, offering 1,000 dollars as a prize.

Billy Robinson took him on, but at the last moment Foo withdrew the challenge and Robinson was unable to show he was just as skilled as the Chinese.

A contract for Chung Ling Soo to appear at the Theatre Royal and Grand, Bolton in August 1915. Soo was such a popular performer that theatres had to book him several years in advance. The contract itself is dated 1913.

There's no doubt that Foo's climb down upset Billy but whether this is what prompted him to 'steal' Foo's act and present it himself we will never know.

An international agent offered him a booking at the Folies Bergère in Paris if he would appear as a Chinese and imitate the genuine article in Ching Ling Foo.

Soo's colourful note paper.

"How about Chung Ling Soo? That's a real Chinese name and it means something too."

"What does it mean, then?"

"Extra Good Luck."

"That's just what I need," said the magician.

And that's how Chung Ling Soo was born.

For the next eighteen years Billy Robinson maintained his role of a Chinese magician both on and off the stage. Only a handful of friends, relatives and employees knew that he wasn't really Chinese at all.

At his London debut he produced doves, turned water into flags, caught live goldfish with a fishing rod thrown out among the audience and produced his big bowl of water without mishap.

Soo's act was the sensation of London. He was given a three months' contract at the old Alhambra Theatre, Leicester Square (now the Odeon). After his opening night he had further bookings in England and Europe for the next five years.

In 1905 at the London Hippodrome, Soo had his tiny wife, now known as Suee Sen, climb into the barrel of a cannon whereupon

Soo spells his name in smoke, though in real life, even Soo couldn't actually achieve such a miracle.

Robinson jumped at the chance, bought himself some Chinese robes, shaved his head and moustache and put the whole of his company into oriental attire and makeup. He called himself Hop Sing Loo.

It was the first time he had performed in heavy Chinese costume and through lack of rehearsals his act was a terrible flop, especially when he almost dropped the huge bowl of water he was producing out of nowhere; it leaked all over the stage.

The American magician and his wife, feeling very depressed, were in their dressing room when there came a knock on the door. The visitor was a London theatrical agent who had been in the audience and had understood that it wasn't all Billy's fault that things had gone wrong.

"I can get you a date in London" he said. "You'll do much better there. But, first, we must change that name. Hop Sing Loo just sounds too awful for words."

"What do you suggest?" asked the dejected conjuror.

she was 'shot' to the back of the theatre. He also performed the trick for which he is best remembered: catching a bullet on a china plate.

At the same time as Soo appeared at the London Hippodrome (later the Talk of the Town restaurant) in Leicester Square, the original Ching Ling Foo headlined a few steps away at the old Empire music hall, now a dance hall and cinema. The genuine Chinese magician was so enraged by his imitator's success he issued a challenge to the effect that he would wager £1,000 if Chung Ling Soo could do ten of his twenty tricks or if he, Ching, failed to do any one of his.

Billy Robinson was quick to hit back. Claiming to be "conjuror to the Dowager Empress of China" — which he certainly was not — he said he would not demean himself by becoming involved with a cheap street busker. The infuriated Chinese magician's next verbal onslaught was to announce that it was he who had entertained the Empress. Ching accused Robinson of being a fake Chinese magician who had secured his bookings on the strength of his own successful performances on his world tours.

A Sunday newspaper organised a magical competition between the two performers. Chung Ling Soo arrived at the paper's offices in Fleet Street eager to win the wager at the expense of the man who had refused to compete in a similar contest in New York a few years previously when Billy was an unknown act.

But the Chinese magician failed to arrive at the editor's office and Billy Robinson, in his role of Chung Ling Soo, was declared the superior magician. He received so much publicity over this challenge that he was kept on at the London Hippodrome for three months. His rival, at the Empire, lasted only four weeks.

During one of his Australian tours he had a British comedy magician on the bill by the name of Fred Culpitt. The two men became friends and Soo gave him a fine looking silk cloth to drape over his stage table. Culpitt asked an expert in oriental languages the meaning of the Chinese writing that had been embroidered on the material. The reply sent him into fits of laughter . . .

"They mean you are a fully paid up member of the Foochow Undertakers' Union."

Soo has one surviving member of his family, his son Hector who is now 73 years old. Hector Robinson was eight years old when his father

Another of Soo's attractive colour posters. These would be pasted outside theatres where he was appearing.

died. He is a respected member of the Magic Circle and has lectured on his father's career both in England and the USA.

Hector followed in his father's footsteps and became an amateur magician. But he admits he was never as good as his famous parent.

He recalls that he was once performing at a party, dressed in complete authentic Chinese garb when a small boy yelled up from the front row, "You're not really a Chinaman, are you?"

Hector had to confess that he wasn't. But in recounting the story he has to admit: "That would never have happened to my father."

The funniest story he tells about his life as a young magician was when he was on top of a bus with three goldfish in a cellophane bag. He'd bought them from a shop and was on his way home to work out how to use them in his

act when a big fellow sat down beside him, crushed the bag, causing it to split. A trickle of water began oozing down the side of his leg. His fellow passenger thought the worst. "You should hop off the bus, my lad," he told him. When young Hector took the bag out of his pocket and produced three live goldfish his companion said, "*Hmmm*, you're a magician as well, are you?" Hector jumped off the bus at the next stop, ran to the nearest shop where he was given a fresh bag— just in time to save the lives of the gasping goldfish.

Chung Ling Soo's most famous trick was the one that killed him on March 23rd 1918, on the stage of the Wood Green Empire, a suburban music hall in North London and now a super-market.

Paul Daniels re-creates the famous catching-a-bullet-on-a-plate act just as Chung Ling Soo performed it on the night he was shot in 1918. This is the most dangerous illusion in the world and has killed 27 magicians.

"The Marvellous Chinese Conjuror from the Land of the Peacock" had been performing it successfully for 14 years prior to his death but the trick has killed 27 magicians and is so dangerous it is seldom performed today.

Very simply it's the most dangerous trick in

50

the world . . . Catching a Bullet!

It's a feat that Hector never saw his father perform since the young Robinson only saw him entertain at children's matinees. And Soo never would include the trick in front of children — it was too dangerous.

On this occasion something went wrong. A bullet pierced Soo's chest and he was taken by ambulance to hospital, where he died.

You can well imagine my feelings when, dressed as a Chinese war lord, I stood in front of a loaded musket for one of my TV programmes a few months ago. The man firing at me was Jack Grossman, now 82, who worked for Soo as one of his stage assistants when he was in his early teens. Mr Grossman came down from his home in Sheffield to help recreate one of the classic tricks in magic.

For it was he who actually fired at Soo on the night he was shot! He has never fired a gun since that night and I don't blame him.

So, in spite of this great danger, what made me attempt this feat? The explanation is that I was surrounded by a great team of professional assistants. The whole trick had been well rehearsed but, even in the studio, we had to make three attempts before getting it right.

Catching a bullet is not a trick for amateurs. You have to be a very experienced performer to attempt to do so. Even after all these years I find it very sad that one of the great magicians of this century should mainly be remembered for the trick that killed him.

Soo was not only a great performer, he did a whole two hour show without speaking a word, but he also took immense trouble to perpetuate his great showmanship with some of the most colourful and intriguing posters and publicity material that the world of show business has ever seen.

Chung Ling Soo's posters have been copied and treasured by magicians throughout the world. The originals attract big sums whenever they are put up for sale.

He billed himself as "Chung Ling Soo — Mysteries from the Land of the Peacock". His posters would announce "Spellbound they gathered, far and near to scan, the weird powers of this wondrous man".

But, perhaps, the most famous description that he gave of himself was "A Gift from the Gods to Mortals on Earth to Amuse and Mystify".

One of his featured illusions was one in which Soo blew puffs of smoke towards an empty glass vase and when it was uncovered it was filled with smoke.

In my TV tribute to this great performer I was able to reproduce this same effect at the opening of the show. It was a trick of which he was especially proud and this is why he had one of his posters specially designed to show the smoke spelling out his name.

It never happened on the stage, of course. Just as I didn't spell out my name with this trick on the Paul Daniels Magic Show.

You'd have to be a *real* magician to do that.

Jack Grossman, one of the two stage assistants who aimed their muskets at Soo on the night he died, takes aim again . . . in a BBC TV studio. Mr Grossman is now a lively 81-year-old living in Sheffield.

DO IT YOURSELF MAGIC

This section is for do-it-yourself enthusiasts. If you're not handy at making things then get a friend to help you.

Most magicians make up tricks for themselves and you don't have to be an expert carpenter or joiner to do the same, but you'll need a grown-up's help for the first one.

THE MATCHING CUBE

Show the audience a Rubik cube, give it a few twists and then place it in a black bag. Invite a member of your audience to put his hands inside the bag and twist it as many times as he likes.

Get two other helpers to do the same, but instruct the final assistant to leave the cube properly squared. The cube is then handed back to you, still inside the bag. This, as you inform your audience, is to ensure you cannot possibly know the final arrangement on any of its sides.

You then take a second cube which has been in view of the audience throughout your performance. Turn the cube around and show the pattern on one side. Place this back on your table with this side showing to the spectators.

Now take the original cube out of the bag and your friends will be astonished to see that the colours on one side of this first cube correspond exactly with the pattern on one side of the second.

This is a very slick, modern trick and very easy to perform. As you may have guessed, you need a fake cube. Here's where some do-it-yourself skill is required. Get yourself a couple of cheap cubes with stick-on coloured patches which peel off easily.

First, revolve the top layer of one cube as shown in my drawing. Then remove the two

52

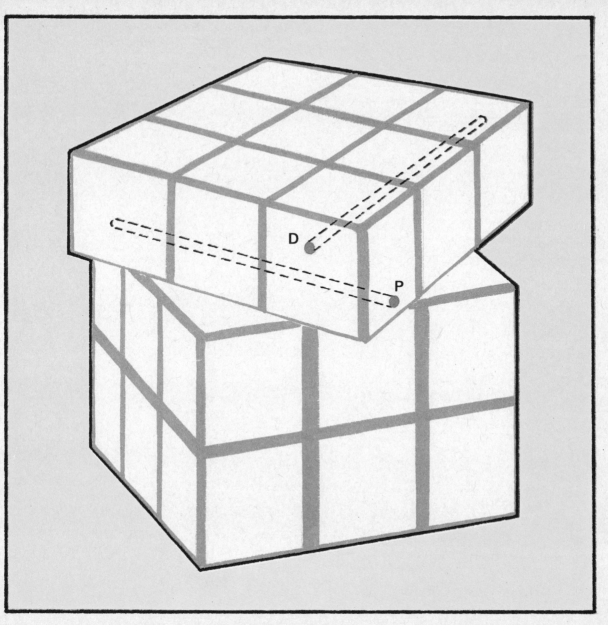

coloured spots marked P and D. Next, a hole has to be drilled through side P as shown in the drawing, large enough to take a two inch nail. Remove the head of the nail, coat it with thick glue and push it into the hole making sure it doesn't protrude from the other end. Let it set firm. Then replace the same coloured label that was there beforehand.

Now do the same through hole D and drill space for a second nail to go through this section in the same position as shown in the illustration.

Glue a second two-inch headless nail through this hold and, when it is firmly set, replace the other coloured label.

You now have a fake Rubic cube which has one side that will always stay the same. So, however much your three assistants twist and turn the cube inside the black bag at the start of the trick, one side will always remain unchanged.

Your final preparation is to take a look at the colours on one of the two immovable sides of your fake cube then peel off the coloured tabs and rearrange

the identical design on one of the sides of your other cube.

Thus, when you show the side of this cube it will exactly match the side of the fake one. Tell your audience it would be quite impossible to foretell correctly all six sides of a Rubik cube — the odds against it are more than 43 million million million to one.

"But I can predict the colours on one side; that's somewhat easier: a mere 1,500,000 to one chance!"

THE FIFTY-TWO CARD TRICK

This is a cheeky pocket trick which will always get you a big laugh. It is quite easy to make up but you'll need the help of a friend with a camera and some knowledge of photography.

First lay out a complete pack of cards in rows, one row for each suit. Also have each suit in order from ace to king.

Using a coloured film, have your friend make a close-up photograph of the whole pack. Then get him to supply you with a small print, just the size of a playing card, showing all the cards in the pack. Paste a real playing card face downwards on the back of the photograph. If you're clever enough to peel off the back, stick that on instead.

Keep this card in your pocket and when you want to show anyone your magical skill just produce your playing card and lay it face downwards on the table.

Invite your friend to name a card. Then, no matter what card he's named, ask him, "Wouldn't you think it a miracle if your card turned up on the face of the one I've just taken from my pocket?"

Your companion is bound to agree. So turn your card over and say, "It's bound to be there somewhere." Then run!

THE TWO TUBES

The magician has two tubes on his table. He shows them to be empty and then puts one inside the other and stands them on his table. Tissue paper is placed over the ends of the two tubes (one inside the other) using a couple of elastic bands, one at each end.

The performer then puts his finger through the paper and pulls out a whole collection of silk handkerchiefs, carnival streamers or what you will. As a climax you can produce a bunch of flowers that spring open when released. These are specially made for magicians and can be obtained at any magic shop.

To bring all this about you will need a couple of cardboard tubes that fit easily inside each other. Use tubes used for posting maps and documents; they can be bought at most stationers. The outer and wider tube remains untouched but the smaller tube needs doctoring beforehand, for it contains a secret cylinder much smaller in diameter. Arrange this smaller tube inside the bigger one so that it is glued along one side as in the illustration.

When this is done, cut a cardboard circle just a little smaller than the main tube. Then using the smallest tube of all as a guide, cut a hole in this circular piece of cardboard so as to give access to the secret cylinder (see drawing).

Paint the inside of all the tubes black as well as the disc you have cut out. When you load the secret compartment take care not to have any bright silks at the top; a black one would be best.

Start your performance by having both cardboard cylinders standing upright, one inside the other one, on your table. Lift off the outer one and put your magic wand right through it to prove that it is empty.

Do the same with the fake tube, inserting your wand through the little hole you have provided for this very purpose.

Now put the empty, unprepared cylinder over the one holding your silks. Fix your tissue paper at both ends; a secret mark on the outside of the top of your tube will tell you which end to break the tissue paper, and produce your silks.

Remember, before sealing

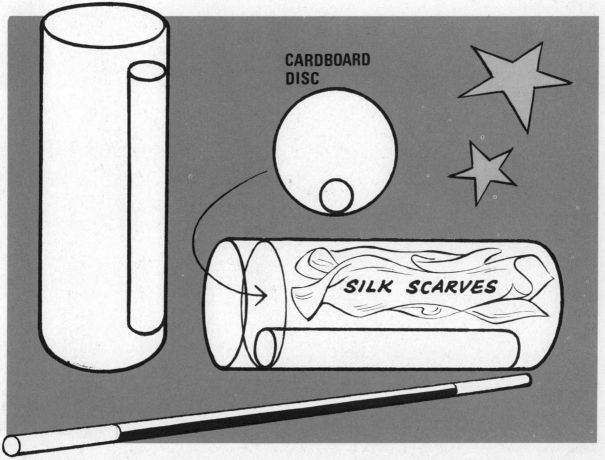

CARDBOARD DISC

SILK SCARVES

both ends, to hold the cylinders carefully when the smaller one is inside the larger, or it may fall out.

Also, make both tubes as attractive on the outside as you can. Decorate them with bright coloured paint or paper.

This particular trick is good, standard magic and well worth the time taken to prepare the apparatus.

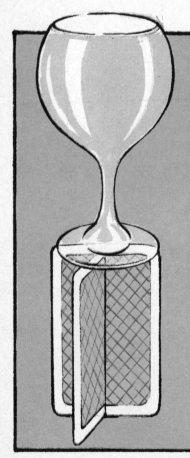

THE TIGHTROPE CARD

Take a card from your pack, say the magic words and it stands upright on your table. This in itself is a remarkable achievement but you now go one better by balancing a wine glass or a matchbox on the edge of the upright card.

You need a trick card for this unusual effect and it's something you'll find very easy to make.

Two cards are used to make the Tightrope Card. First, you have to make a slight impression down the back of one of them from top to bottom so that it will bend easily. Use a sharp penknife and a ruler. Glue the face of one side of this card and press it to the back of the second card.

You'll now have a card with a flap. With the flap held down it looks like any ordinary card but with the flap extended you can place it with its face to the audience and it will stand upright.

Keep your trick card in your pack and when you take it out you can show both the face and the back to your audience. Open the flap as you place the glass in position, apparently on the edge of the playing card. Then, when you remove the glass with your right hand pick up the card with your left hand and with your forefinger just close the flap.

The audience will only see an ordinary playing card being replaced in the pack.

THE HALF-AND-HALF CARDS

To make a half-and-half card, cut a card across diagonally and glue one half of it over one half of another card. This will enable you to perform several tricks which can be quite mystifying.

First, make up three half-and-half cards using three queens and three aces. You'll then have three cards split into a queen and an ace. Also required: the remaining queen and the remaining ace in their whole, original form.

Arrange the cards with the queens showing and the aces hidden. The whole queen is on the right of the pile with the whole ace behind.

Fan the cards so that your audience clearly see the queens, making sure you keep hidden the ace half of the three doctored cards.

Close the fan into a small pile and turn it upside down so that only the back of the cards are seen. Remove the front card (the whole queen) and place it behind the others.

If you now fan the cards again they will appear as four aces, for the three half queens and the whole queen have now been hidden.

As a climax throw the four cards, one by one, into your hat, keeping their backs to the audience. Count "one, two, three, four" as you do so.

Practise these moves until they run smoothly. For a variation you can make up your half-and-half cards still using the queen but, for the other half, use a plain card of a low domination such as a three or two. You can then present your trick with the following story.

"Once upon a time there were four beautiful queens who lived in a beautiful castle (show the queens). Now these queens were very vain creatures and whenever their knights went off to the Crusades they used to dress themselves up in their finest clothes, wear their finest jewels and have wonderful banquets, while outside their beautiful castle the poor peasants were starving.

"One day a witch came along and told them, 'Unless you stop your parties, take off your fine clothes and your diamonds and return to your spinning wheels while your knights are away, I'll put a curse upon you.'

"'Oh,' said the queens, 'we don't believe you. What curse could a silly old woman like you put on four beautiful queens like us?'

"'I'll take away your crowns and change you into plain

common folk, all four of you,' replied the witch, and off she went on her broomstick.

"But, sad to say, the queens took no notice. They still wore fine clothes and had wonderful banquets. After a short while the witch returned.

"As the sound of their revelry reached her from within the castle she said the magic words to turn the four queens into plain commoners. They lost their crowns. They lost their fine clothes and they had to live just like the rest of us."

Fan the four plain cards and drop them one by one into the hat.

If you enjoy telling stories while performing then here's another one for you; again using the half-and-half card idea. For this you'll need to take say the queen of hearts, and on the back glue three strips of these cards — another queen of hearts, queen of diamonds and the jack of diamonds. Have just enough of each card running straight down from top to bottom so that it can be identified. You'll also need the jack of hearts with the queen of diamonds glued on the opposite side.

Fan the three glued strips and the separate jack of hearts so that they look like four cards. Place them in your hat. Then remove the two queens, after which you can show the hat empty . . . the jacks have followed the queens and also left.

For this display of your magical skill I suggest you entertain your friends with this little tale:

"Once upon a time there were two queens who were invited out to dinner by two jacks (fan the cards). They went to a very smart restaurant (put them in the hat) where, unfortunately, they had a terrible meal. The food was bad, the service was awful and the bill was enormous.

"When the time came to pay the bill they sent for the manager and told him they had no intention of paying him a single penny. 'In that case,' said the restaurant owner, 'I will keep you all here until you do pay.'

"'You can't keep us,' said the two ladies. 'We're queens, we never pay any bills.'

"So the restaurant owner let the two ladies leave (take out the queens) and escorted them to their carriage.

"This, of course, left the two jacks behind to pay the bill. But these jacks were rather clever fellows, you could say they were knaves, for when the owner of the restaurant returned he found the jacks had climbed out of the window . . ."

Show empty hat.

THE TURN AROUND TRICK

You'll need a pack of cards in which most of the points of the pip cards can be turned to point upwards (see illustration). Look at the pack beforehand and see if this can be done. The easiest cards with which to work are the 3,5,6,7 and 9 of spades, clubs or hearts.

Lay a few of these out before you on the table and you'll see that you can place a card like the three of hearts, for example, so that one heart will point down while the other two will point upwards. With a 9 you'll find you can place it so that four of the symbols can point down but the remaining five are upwards.

Knowing this, it's easy to arrange your cards so that the greater number of symbols on each card point upwards while the lesser number point downwards.

If any card is turned around you'll see at once that these symbols (hearts, clubs or spades) will then be pointing in the opposite direction.

Apart from the 6, you are using odd cards, so it's easy to remember that it's always the *odd number of symbols which are grouped* to point in the same direction. In the case of the 6, you'll discover that two of the symbols point one way and

the other four point to the opposite.

Unless your audience are aware of this, and few of them are likely to be, you can baffle them very easily by inviting someone to turn any card around while your back is turned.

When they've done so, face your audience again and you will see at a glance which card has been moved.

THE TRICK PACK

You can make yourself a fine trick pack of cards which will enable you to do a number of tricks if you have a friend with a stationer's guillotine. If not, shops providing a copying service will have such a machine which is used for cutting paper.

Buy a new pack of cards and trim the whole pack intact by removing a tiny sliver from each side of the pack but at one end only (see illustration). This will have the effect of making one end slightly narrower than the other, but only have the merest trifle sliced off each side.

You now have a truly miracle pack of cards. The tricks you can perform are endless. Here are just a few:

First, ensure all the cards are pointing the right way with the wider part at one end and the thinner at the other. Have someone take a card, look at it and restore it to the pack. Your friend can immediately shuffle and cut the cards as many times as he likes but you will still be able to pick out the selected card.

How's it done? Turn the pack round when he takes the card and when he has returned it you can feel between your finger and thumb just where his card is. The wide end of the card will be protruding slightly from the narrow end of the pack.

A spectacular use of your trick pack would be to let him return the card to the pack (which you've turned round) and then hold the pack in your right hand before letting all the cards fall on the floor, retaining the chosen card between forefinger and thumb.

You could also cut the cards yourself after the chosen card has been returned, cutting at

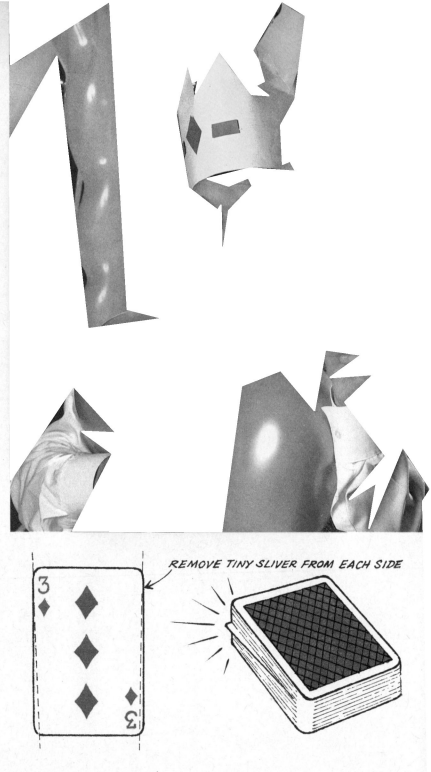

REMOVE TINY SLIVER FROM EACH SIDE

this same selected card which will be at the bottom of the top section of cards cut. A quick glance will tell you its identity. Have the pack cut and shuffled by your friend, put your hand to your head and name the card.

"I just picked up the mental image of your card that you had

in your mind," you tell him. He'll probably believe you too!

If you find this trick pack too difficult to make, you can buy a pack already made up for you and many more tricks as well in the Paul Daniels range available at any good toy shop or department store.

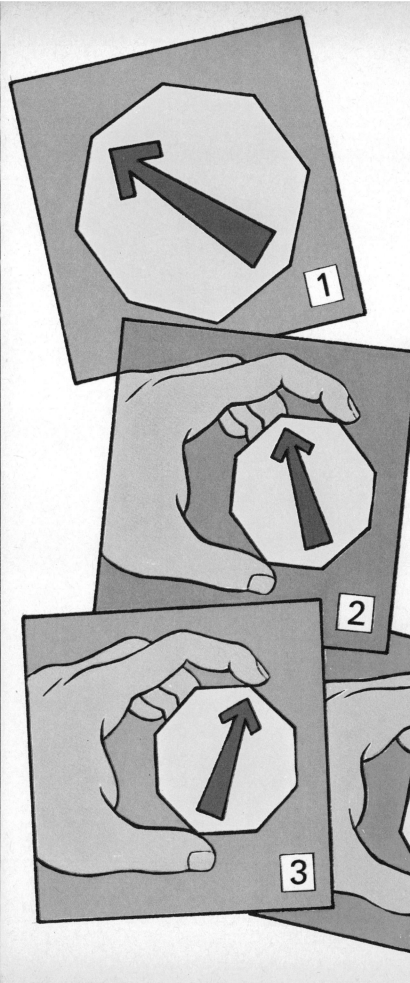

THE CHANGING ARROW

You can make this pocket trick quite easily. Trace the outline of picture 1 onto a piece of cardboard and carefully cut out the eight sided shape. Draw the arrow as in the illustration, then turn over the cardboard and draw another arrow on the other side BUT MAKE SURE THAT YOU DRAW IT AT RIGHT ANGLES TO THE FIRST ARROW. Right angles means, for example, that if one arrow is pointing at 12 o'clock the other arrow is pointing at 3 o'clock.

Now by holding the cardboard at opposite points rotate the 'compass' to show the other side. Dependant upon which of the corners you hold the arrows seem to point in different directions to each other. Pictures 2, 3, and 4 demonstrate the different holds.

If you find this trick pack too difficult to make, you can buy a pack already made up for you and many more tricks as well in the Paul Daniels range available at any good toy shop or department store.

61